DISCOVERIES

# The Human Body

## STICKER BOOK

BARNES & NOBLE

NEW YORK

# Studying the body

The human body has proven to be a source of endless fascination for us. Inventions such as microscopes, thermometers, and stethoscopes now help us explore the body more closely than ever before.

## Stethoscope

A stethoscope is used to listen to the rhythmic beating of the human heart. Before it was invented, doctors would listen to hearts by placing their ears to their patients' chests.

## Microscope

Without the microscope, we would not have discovered that the human body is made up of billions of cells. Even the tiniest cell can be enlarged with a microscope so that its parts become visible.

## Venus of Willendorf

This Stone Age fertility statue shows how people have been fascinated with the shape of the human body for centuries.

## Digital thermometer

A thermometer measures temperature. The normal temperature for the human body is around 98.6°F (37°C).

## Fossilized skull

Fossilized bones, like this skull, are studied to gain insight into the evolution of the human race.

## Hieroglyphs

The ancient Egyptians used these symbols, or hieroglyphs, to represent the uterus—a part of the female reproductive system.

## Muscular structure

Dozens of muscles lie just under the skin and people have long studied the structure and movement of these muscles. The skeletal muscles make up two-fifths of your body weight.

## False teeth

Doctors and engineers can now replace nonworking or decayed body parts with artificial replicas. False teeth allow those without teeth to chew and eat normally.

# The control center

The body has an elaborate control center, the brain, which receives messages from various parts of the body via neurons, or nerve cells. The brain processes all this information and replies with instructions.

## The brain
The brain is divided into two hemispheres. The left hemisphere coordinates the right side of the body and the right hemisphere, the left side of the body.

## Synapse
The tiny gap between nerve cells is known as the synapse. Chemicals ferry messages across this gap.

## Brain stem—from the front
The brain stem regulates involuntary functions such as breathing, the beating of the heart, and salivation.

## The spinal cord
The spinal cord is about as thick as your index finger. It is like an information highway that connects the brain and peripheral nervous system.

## Brain stem—from the side
The brain stem forms the main pathway of communication between the brain and spinal cord.

## Neuron
Neurons, or nerve cells, are located in the brain, the spinal cord, and parts of the peripheral nervous system.

## Nerve cell
Nerve cells form a communication matrix between all parts of the body and the brain.

## Neural network
Spidery dendrites branch out from each nerve cell in a neural network that allows signals to travel from cell to cell.

# The vital systems

The circulatory, respiratory, and digestive systems carry out all the vital bodily processes—pumping blood, breathing, and processing food—ensuring that the body is able function properly.

### Intestines
Nutrients and water from the food we ingest are extracted in the intestines.

### Inside a cell
Most cells are made up of an outer skin, or membrane, holding a jelly-like fluid within which sits the control center, or nucleus, of the cell.

### Small intestine
The small intestine takes in the semi-digested food from the stomach where enzymes help break the food down further.

### Inside the lungs
The lungs are made up of thousands of little branches, or bronchioles, that channel the air we breathe through our lungs.

### Lungs
Oxygen—vital for the energy giving chemical reactions that occur in each cell—is absorbed by the lungs from the air we inhale.

### Stomach
The stomach's lining contains tiny glands that make gastric acids, enzymes, and mucus that begin the process of digestion.

### Inside the heart
The heart is a powerful, double-chambered pump that sends blood through to the arteries and around the body.

### Kidneys
The kidneys filter 42 gallons (19a0 liters) of blood every day. The waste and excess water are excreted through the urinary system.

### Capillary
Capillaries are very fine blood vessels. Their thin walls allow oxygen, nutrients, and sugars in the blood to seep through to surrounding cells.

### Artery
Arteries take oxygenated blood from the heart to the rest of the body. They have thick, elastic walls so they can withstand the pressure of blood surging from the heart.

### Vein
Veins carry blood back to the heart so that it can be re-oxygenated. Veins have a one-way valve that prevents blood from flowing away from the heart.

### Around the liver
The pancreas, gall bladder, and liver assist in the digestive process. The liver is the largest organ in the body. It has more than 600 different jobs.

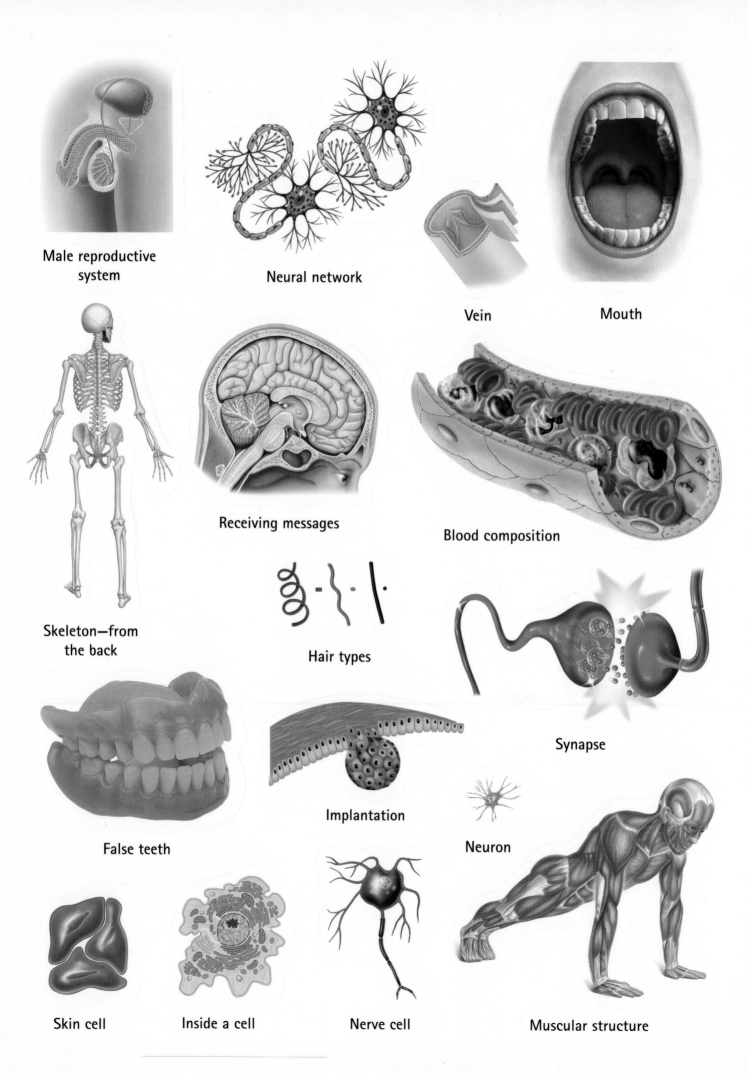

Male reproductive
system

Neural network

Vein

Mouth

Skeleton—from
the back

Receiving messages

Blood composition

Hair types

Synapse

False teeth

Implantation

Neuron

Skin cell

Inside a cell

Nerve cell

Muscular structure

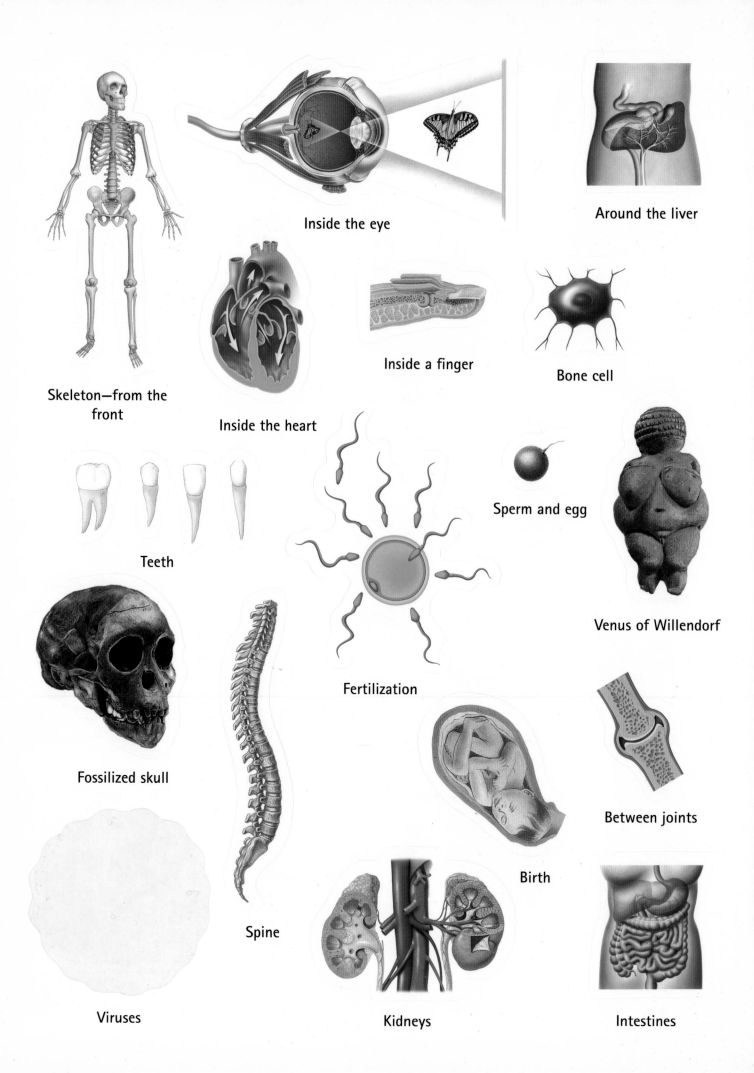

Skeleton—from the front

Inside the eye

Around the liver

Inside the heart

Inside a finger

Bone cell

Teeth

Sperm and egg

Venus of Willendorf

Fossilized skull

Fertilization

Spine

Birth

Between joints

Viruses

Kidneys

Intestines

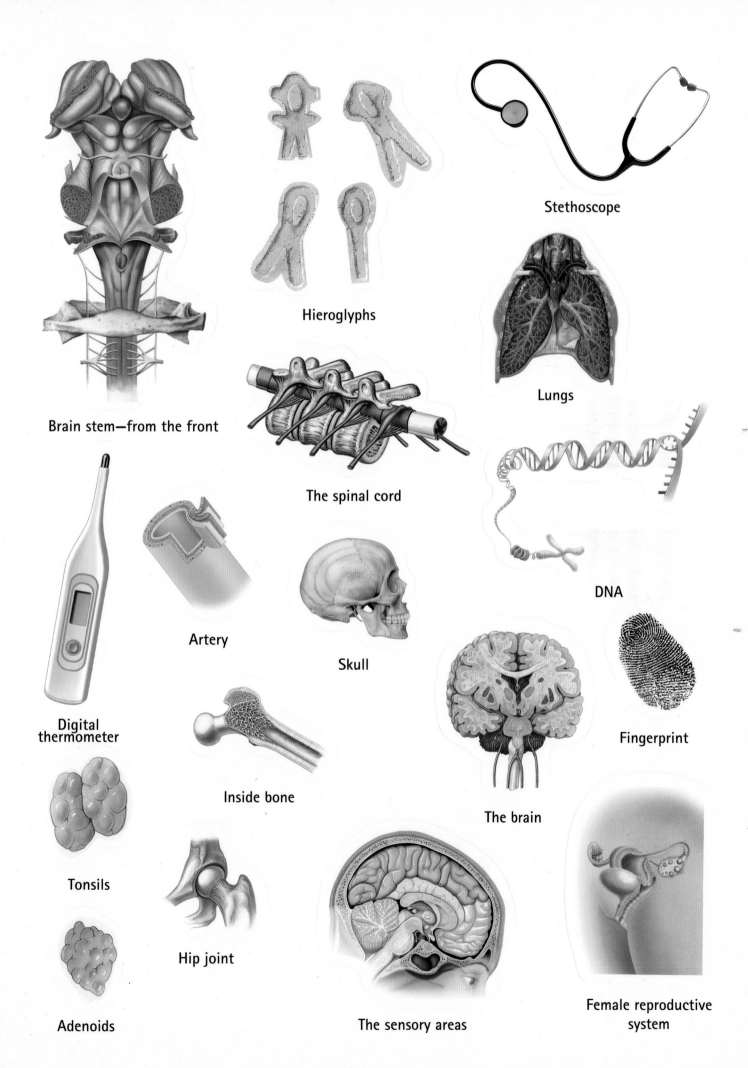

Brain stem—from the front

Hieroglyphs

Stethoscope

Lungs

The spinal cord

DNA

Digital thermometer

Artery

Skull

The brain

Fingerprint

Inside bone

Tonsils

Hip joint

The sensory areas

Adenoids

Female reproductive system

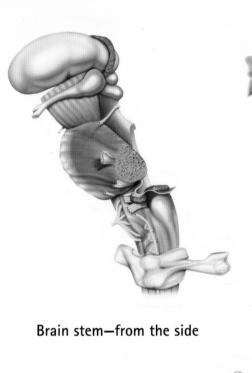

Brain stem—from the side

Small intestine

Hair follicle

Capillary

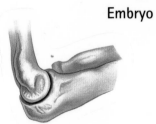

Inside the ear

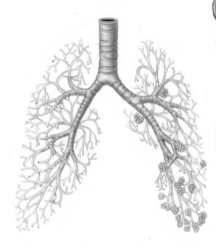

Inside the lungs

Ear bones

Microscope

Embryo

Eye

Elbow joint

Stomach

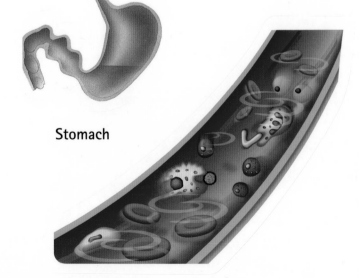

Immune system

Boil

Fetus

# The bare bones

The outer structure of the body is formed by the bones, skin, hair, and teeth. These parts of the body are instrumental in holding us together, keeping us warm, and helping us move and eat.

## Hip joint
The hip is a ball-and-socket joint that moves back and forth, and from side to side.

## Teeth
We have four different types of teeth: incisors are wide and sharp to cut and bite; canines are long and pointed to tear and rip at food; premolars and molars are broader and flatter for chewing and crushing.

## Hair follicle
Hair grows out of the skin through hair follicles.

## Skeleton—from the front
The skeleton forms the stiff and strong inner framework of the body.

## Skeleton—from the back
The skeleton is made up of 206 bones, all of which work together to help us move.

## Elbow joint
The elbow is a hinge joint, which means that it only allows to-and-fro movement.

## Spine
The 24 vertebrae of the spine are cushioned by washer-like disks of flexible cartilage.

## The skull
The skull has a rounded dome that shields the delicate brain from injury.

## Hair types
The kind of hair you have depends on the shape of each strand's end. A strand of curly hair looks square; wavy hair looks oval; and straight hair looks circular.

## Inside bone
Bone can be likened to a tube. The outside is hard while the inside contains a jelly-like tissue, known as bone marrow.

## Skin cell
The body's tough surface, the dermis, is made up of flat, hard, and dead skin cells. Underneath the dermis lies a layer of live skin cells—the epidermis.

## Inside a finger
Like hair, our nails are dead, and it is the nail bed and surrounding skin that sense touch and pressure.

## Between joints
Smooth cartilage coats the end of each bone at a joint. A slippery fluid moistens the joint and tough ligaments hold it together.

## Bone cell
Bone cells are spidery in shape. These cells build and maintain the collagen and mineral crystals that make up bone.

# The beginnings

## It's hard to imagine that a living, breathing, thinking human being emerged from what was once a tiny cell.

### Birth
At nine months when the baby is ready to be born, strong uterine movements push it through the vagina into the world.

### Implantation
It takes about seven days from fertilization for the dividing zygote to attach to the wall of the uterus.

### Fertilization
Sperm cells meet the egg and burrow in. The first sperm to penetrate fertilizes the egg. Once fertilized the egg blocks all other sperm. The fertilized egg is now called a zygote.

### Male reproductive system
Male testes, or testicles, are oval in shape and contain cells that continually divide to form millions of sperm cells every day.

### Embryo
When it reaches seven weeks, the unborn child is called an embryo.

### Female reproductive system
Each month, one ovum, or egg, ripens and passes along the Fallopian tubes to the uterus or womb.

### Fetus
At two months, the embryo becomes a fetus. At this stage it's about the size of a walnut.

### Sperm and egg
The moment of conception is when a sperm fertilizes an egg.

### DNA
DNA is the chemical that contains all your genetic information like hair color, height, and eye color. It is stored on 46 chromosomes that are twisted in pairs inside every one of your cells.

# Under attack

The human body has a number of defense systems to protect it against disease. Each system works to prevent germs, viruses, and other attackers from invading and infecting the body.

## Tonsils

Tonsils help fight off infections that affect the pharynx and the respiratory tract. They are found at the back of the throat.

## Blood composition

Blood is made up of red blood cells, white blood cells, and platelets. White cells attack bacteria, so if you're fighting an infection your white cell count will increase.

## Viruses

Viruses work by tricking our cells into making more virus cells. This process changes a normal cell's chemical makeup, either damaging or killing it.

## Adenoids

Adenoids lie behind the nose waiting to trap the infections and bacteria we inhale along with air.

## Immune system

The immune system is the body's internal defense system. It makes proteins known as antibodies that stick to and destroy invaders of the body like bacteria and viruses.

## Boil

Bacteria that gathers in a hair follicle can cause it to become infected. The infection results in a tender, inflamed lump called a boil.

# Sensing the world

The body is equipped to experience and enjoy the outside world via the five senses—sight, sound, taste, touch, and smell. Each sensation causes information to be sent to the brain for processing.

## Ear bones
These are the tiniest bones in the body. Ear bones transmit vibrations from the eardrum to the cochlea which sends the sound information to the brain.

## Eye
Two-thirds of all the information processed by the human brain comes in through our eyes.

## Fingerprint
The ridges and wrinkles on your fingertips are unique to you. They also provide traction for grasping and feeling objects.

## Mouth
The mouth consists of the tongue, whose small lumps and bumps (called papillae) help grip food; tiny taste buds that detect flavors; and lips that determine the temperatures of food.

## The sensory areas
The brain transforms the rush of information from your senses to what we experience and how we experience it through our thoughts, hopes, and feelings.

## Receiving messages
The brain combines messages from all the senses and runs them through its memory banks. This allows us to learn and grow.

## Inside the eye
The main part of the eyeball is filled with a clear, jelly-like fluid that keeps the eye firm and well-shaped. Eye muscles behind the eyeball move it within its bony skull socket.

## Inside the ear
The outer ear guides sound waves into the ear canal. This aural information enters the middle ear where it is amplified and sent via the eardrum to the inner ear and to the brain.